Bud's Boo

Written by Rozanne Lanczak Williams
Created by Sue Lewis
Illustrated by Patty Briles

Creative Teaching Press

Bud's Book of Five
© 2002 Creative Teaching Press, Inc.
Written by Rozanne Lanczak Williams
Illustrated by Patty Briles
Project Manager: Sue Lewis
Project Director: Carolea Williams

Published in the United States of America by:
Creative Teaching Press, Inc.
P.O. Box 2723
Huntington Beach, CA 92647-0723

ISBN: 1-57471-876-2
CTP 3242

Five, five, five!

Five bees in a hive.

Five bikes to ride.

Five monkeys on the slide.

Five kites in the sky—
flying high.

Five spots on five
little butterflies.

Five shiny lights in the night.

Five little bears say,
"Good night!"

Create your own book!

Write and illustrate your own book of five.

Words in *Bud's Book of Five*

Long *i*		High-Frequency Words	Other
five	sky	of	book
hive	flying	in	Bud's
ride		a	bees
bikes		to	monkeys
kites		on	spots
slide		the	bears
butterflies		little	good
high		say	
lights			
night			
shiny			